Len and Anne Frobisher

Heinemann
Halley Court, Jordan Hill, Oxford, OX2 8EJ
a division of Reed Educational and Professional Publishing Ltd
www.heinemann.co.uk

Heinemann is a registered trademark of Reed Educational and Professional Publishing Ltd

ISBN 0 435 20864 0 (Pupil Book)
ISBN 0 435 20872 1 (Teacher's version)

09 08 07 06 05 04 03

Illustrated by Garry Davies

Cover illustration by Andrew Hunt

Typesetting and layout by DP Press Ltd, Sevenoaks, Kent

Printed by Ebenezer Baylis, Worcester

Contents

WORD PROBLEMS YEAR 3

Number problems 1

1 Jane has 2 books of 100 stickers, 1 book of 10 stickers and 5 single stickers.

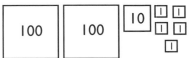

How many stickers has she altogether? **215**

2 There are 9 crayons in a red box and 16 in a blue box.

Which box has more crayons? **blue**
How many more? **7**

3 Shahid estimates that there are 60 marbles in a jar.

Anna thinks there are 10 more that that. What is Anna's estimate? **70**

4 Between pages 248 and 251 some pages are missing.

What are the numbers of the missing pages? **249, 250**

5 Four runners in a race have the numbers 198, 918, 819 and 891.

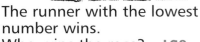

The runner with the lowest number wins.
Who wins the race? **198**

6 Robin has 481 stamps in a large book. He puts 100 of them into a smaller book.

481

How many stamps are left in the larger book? **381**

7

*I am an odd number.
I am between 48 and 51.*

What am I?

49

Money problems 1

❶ On a cake stall buns cost 4p each.

Sammy buys 5 buns. How much do the five buns cost her? **20p**

She pays with a 50p coin.

How much change does she get? **30p**

❷ The comic Blitz costs £2.

Sol buys two Blitz comics. What change does he get from a £5 note? **£1**

❸ Animal badges cost 3p each. Stef wants to buy four badges. How much money does he need? **12p**

❹ For her birthday Alice is given two £5 notes. How much money is she given altogether? **£10**

❺ In her purse Katie has three 2p coins.

How much has she in her purse? **6p**

❻ Each week Winston saves a 5p coin. Altogether he has saved 25p.

For how many weeks has he saved? **5**

❼

I am a round, silver coin. I am between 5p and 20p.

What am I?

10p

Number problems 2

1 In a packet there are 24 daffodil bulbs and 23 tulip bulbs.

How many bulbs are there altogether in the packet?   47

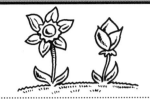

2 A bike has two wheels.

How many wheels are there on nine bikes?   18

3 On Monday Rachel buys 14 stickers. On Tuesday she buys double that number.

How many stickers does she buy on Tuesday?   28

4 James has a tube of 30 Zunts. He eats half of them.

How many Zunts has he left?   15

5 There are 13 biscuits on a plate. Tim eats 4 of them and Sally eats 3 of them.

How many biscuits are left?   6

6 A box has 56 pencils. Harriet puts in another 8 pencils.

How many pencils are in the box now?   64

7

I am a number. If I add 7 to my number and double the answer I get 20.

What am I?

3

Time problems 1

1 A basketball game started at 2:15 p.m. It lasted for 35 minutes.

What time did it end?

start:	2:15
end:	**2:50**

2 A bus passes the school every 5 minutes. The first bus passes at 8 o'clock.

Every 5 minutes

How many more buses will pass in the next 30 minutes? **6**

3 Playtime begins at 10:25. It ends at 10:50.

How long does playtime last? **25 minutes**

4 In a test Ruth answers one question every 5 minutes.

How long does it take her to answer 8 questions? **40 minutes**

5 After 1 a.m. a plane goes from London to New York every 5 hours.

How many planes go from London to New York in one day? **4**

6 A train journey takes 2 hours 15 minutes. It ends at 1 p.m.

What time did the train leave the station? **10.45 a.m.**

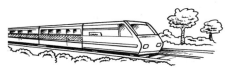

7

I am between 8:20 and quarter to 9. My minutes are an odd multiple of 10.

What am I?

8:30

Number problems 3

❶ The result of a rugby match was 9 points to 4.

result
9 – 4

What was the points difference between the two scores? **5**

❷ A baker has 10 tarts for sale. He sells two of them.

How many tarts has he left? **8**

❸ Three children have come to Lisa's party. Soon 7 more children arrive.

How many children have come to Lisa's party? **10**

❹ On one side of a road there are 4 houses. On the other side of the road there are 5 houses.

How many houses are there altogether on the road? **9**

❺ Rashid sells 12 tickets for the school concert. Amy sells 8 tickets.

How many tickets have they sold altogether? **20**

❻ Harry scores 16 points. He needs 20 points to win the game.

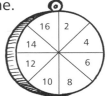

How many more points does he need to win the game? **4**

❼

I have two digits. My units digit is 2. I am less than 20.

What am I?

12

Length problems 1

❶ In a 400 metres race a runner has 100 metres left to run.

How many metres has she run? **300**

❷ Nila cuts a piece of ribbon into two lengths, 32 cm and 27 cm.

How long was the ribbon before she cut it? **59 cm**

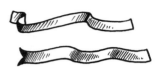

❸ A 28 cm length of wood is cut into two equal lengths.

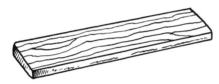

What is the length of each piece? **14 cm**

❹ A tape measure is marked in metres on one side. On the other side it is marked in centimetres.

How many centimetres are on the other side to 2.5 metres? **250 cm**

❺ A bike race is 10 times round a 125 metres track.

How long is the race?

1250 m

❻ A 40 cm lamp is put on a 1 metre high table.

What is the height of the top of the lamp from the ground? **1.4 m**

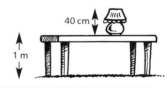

40 cm
1 m

❼ *I am a length between 3 and 6 metres. My length in cm has 3 even digits which are all the same.*

What am I?

444 cm

Review problems 1

Marathon result

1	J Matabu	367	2 hr 17 min
2	S Collier	746	2 hr 19 min
3	F Wanavi	607	2 hr 39 min
4	H Bell	271	2 hr 58 min
5	R Tibinali	712	3 hr 08 min

Ladies Long Jump result

1	W Askew	692	11 m 33 cm
2	B Sambu	489	11 m 17 cm
3	N Roster	361	10 m 40 cm
4	R Harris	279	10 m 11 cm
5	T Weston	481	9 m 48 cm

Entrance

Adult	£5
Children	£2
School groups	£30 per class

1 What is the entrance cost for a family of 2 adults and 3 children? **£16**

2 Stanley Primary School brings 3 classes to the athletics meeting. How much does it cost the school? **£90**

3 Which runner in the marathon had 6 as the units digit of his number? **S Collier**

4 What is the number of the jumper in the long jump that has an odd hundreds digit? **361**

5 In the marathon 300 runners started the race, but only 250 finished. How many did not finish the race? **50**

6 A child from Stanley School said, 'It would take me twice as long as Tibinali to run the marathon.' How long is that? **6 hr 16 min**

7 By how many minutes did Matabu win the marathon? **2 min**

8 The sixth finisher in the marathon finished 60 minutes after the winner. What was his finishing time? **3 hr 17 min**

9 By how many centimetres did W Askew win the long jump? **16 cm**

10 How many centimetres did R Harris jump? **1011 cm**

11 Ros estimated the number of people watching to be 200. The actual number was 700 more than this. How many were watching the athletics? **900**

12 At the start of the athletics there were 70 cars in the car park. In the next hour another 30 cars arrived. How many cars were in the car park at that time? **100**

13 There were 10 coaches in the coach park. Each coach had 50 people. How many people came in coaches? **500**

Number problems 4

odd/even;
repeated addition;
arrays; +/– facts to 20

1 The houses on one side of a street have odd numbers in order. Salim lives in Number 1.

Alice lives four houses from Salim.
What is Alice's number?   9

2 Felicity puts out her toy sheep together in twos. She does this seven times.

How many sheep does she put out altogether?   14

3 On a sheet of paper is a grid of 1 cm squares. The grid has 3 rows and 7 columns.

How many 1 cm squares are on the paper?   21

4 Franky planned her birthday party. She invited 15 girls and 4 boys, but 6 of them could not come.

How many children came to her party?   13

5 At an airport 18 people are waiting to get on a plane. There are only 6 passenger seats left.

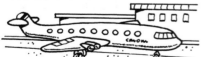

How many will not be able to get on the plane?   12

6 Rob has 12 coins in his piggy bank. He is given 3 more coins.

How many coins has he now?   15

7

I am a two-digit number. My tens digit is half of my units digit. Both digits are even and less than 8.

What am I?

24

Money problems 2

1 A bus ticket costs 65p. How much would two tickets cost? **£1.30**

2 Saul has two 10p coins and one 50p coin.

How much more does he need to buy an 80p ice cream? **10p**

3 Sarah's mum buys both the television and the video recorder.

£700 £300

How much does she pay? **£1000**

4 Harry uses a £10 note to buy a £7 Gameboy.

£7

How much change does he get? **£3**

5 Wari's dad has saved £600 to buy the car. He is saving £100 each week.

For how many more weeks does he need to save? **4**

£1000

6 Su saves 20p of her pocket money every week.

How many pounds will she have saved after 10 weeks? **2**

7

What am I? I am an amount of money. The total of one each of every kind of coin makes me.

What am I?

£3.88

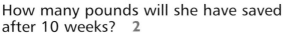

13

Number problems 5

1 Gary scores 53 runs in a cricket match. Emma scores 10 more runs than Gary.

How many runs does Emma score?

63

2 Children are taken on holiday in 100 taxis. Each taxi has 4 children.

How many children go on holiday? **400**

3 On Monday 487 planes land at an airport. On Tuesday 100 more land than on Monday.

How many planes land on Tuesday? **587**

4 Ayesha sells 60 cakes at the school fair. This is 10 less than she estimated.

How many did Ayesha estimate she would sell? **70**

5 In each box there are 20 pencils.

How many pencils are there in 10 boxes?

200

6 Shazad sold 210 raffle tickets. Justin sold 100 less than Shazad.

How many raffle tickets did Justin sell? **110**

7

I am a two-digit even number. I am a multiple of 5. My tens digit is 8 more than my units digit. What am I?

80

14

Number problems 6

1 John breaks one of his four toy cars.

What fraction of his cars are broken? $\frac{1}{4}$

2 There are 40 dogs at a dog show. One-quarter of the dogs are poodles.

How many of the dogs are poodles? 10

3 Wallshill score 6 goals in a football match. Headby score half that number.

How many goals do Headby score? 3

4 Helen has 15 stickers. Emma has double that.

How many stickers has Emma? 30

5 A storm breaks one-tenth of the 200 windows in a block of flats.

How many windows are broken in the flats? 20

6 Jake makes 8 sandwiches. His mother says that they need double that number.

How many sandwiches are needed? 16

7

I am a fraction. My top number is 1 less than my bottom number. My top number is the smallest even number.

What am I?

$\frac{2}{3}$

Time problems 2

1 Children go to a school for 40 weeks in each year.

How many weeks holiday do the children have in a year? **12**

2 Darren can stand on one leg for 1 min 40 sec.

For how many more seconds does Darren need to stand on one leg to do it for 2 minutes? **20 sec**

3 In a whole day Lucia sleeps for 11 hours.

For how many hours is Lucia awake in the day? **13 hours**

4 Jodie goes on her roller skates for a 1 hour ride.

How long has she still to go after 51 minutes? **9 minutes**

5 When going on holiday Amanda spends 9 hours on a plane and 4 hours on a ship.

How many hours does she travel altogether? **13 hours**

6 Khadim watches two TV programmes. The first lasts for 25 minutes, the second for 26 minutes.

For how long does he watch TV? **51 minutes**

7 *I am a two-digit number of minutes. The sum of the digits is 8. My units digit is 3 times my tens digit.*

What am I?

26 min

16

Number problems 7

1 In a game of darts Claire needs 91 to win. She scores 89.

What number does she need to score to win? **2**

2 In a school playground there are 402 children. At 9 o'clock 396 of them go into school.

How many children are left in the playground? **6**

3 Peter shares 48 flowers equally into two vases.

How many flowers are in each vase? **24**

4 There are 5 toes on a foot.

How many toes are there on 7 feet? **35**

5 Lucy has only 5p coins in her money box. Altogether she has 50p.

How many 5p coins has she in her money box? **10**

6 Ten biscuits fit on each plate.

How many plates are needed for 80 biscuits? **8**

7

I am a two-digit number.
I am double an odd number.
My units digit is half of my tens digit.

What am I?

42

Review problems 2

Open 10am – Closed 6pm

Tyrannosaurus rex
13 m, 6 tonnes

Diplodocus
27 m, 12 tonnes

Triceratops
9 m, 5 tonnes

Dimetrodon
3 m, 2 tonnes

1 A baby Diplodocus is 1 metre long.
How many metres does it grow to become full size? **26 m**

2 How many Dimetrodons make the same length as one Triceratops? **3**

3 Write the names of the dinosaurs in order of length, longest first. **Diplodocus, Tyrannosaurus, Triceratops, Dimetrodon**

4 Write the names of the dinosaurs in order of weight, lightest first. **Dimetrodon, Triceratops, Tyrannosaurus, Diplodocus**

5 How many metres longer is a Tyrannosaurus rex than a Triceratops? **4 m**

6 An egg laid by a Tyrannosaurus rex was like a very big sausage. It was 40 cm long and 15 cm wide.
How many centimeters longer than wide was an egg? **25 cm**

7 A class of 30 children visit the museum. It costs each of them 50p to go in.
What is the total cost for the 30 children? **£15**

8 The children walk in pairs to the museum.
How many pairs do 30 children make? **15**

9 The children take a lift to the café. The lift holds 10 children.
How many times will the lift be needed to take all 30 children? **3**

10 The class leave the school at half-past 10. They spend 4 hours out of school. At what time do they arrive back at school?
Half-past 2

11 For how many hours is the museum open? **8 hours**

Number problems 8

❶ Cotford School has 289 children. Salton School has 298 children.

Which school has more children? **Salton**

How many more? **9**

❷ There are 13 people on a bus. At the next stop 8 more get on.

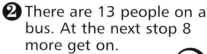

How many people are on the bus now? **21**

❸ Along a road there are 14 lamps. Only 9 of them are working.

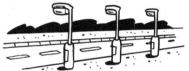

How many lamps are not working? **5**

❹ On Thursday Imran laid 612 bricks. On Friday he laid 621 bricks.

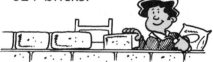

On which day did he lay fewer bricks? **Thursday**

How many fewer? **9**

❺ There are 9 flats in one block and 8 in the other block.

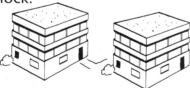

How many flats in the two blocks altogether? **17**

❻ At a party there were 18 bottles of juice. The children drank 12 bottles.

How many bottles were not drunk? **6**

❼

*I am between 100 and 200.
My tens digit is 7.
I am an odd multiple of 10*

What am I?

170

Money problems 3

1 Ennis buys a plant for her mum. The plant costs £3.80.
How much change does she get from £5? **£1.20**

£3.80

2 Perry buys a T-shirt for £2.90 and a cap for £1.50.
How much does she pay altogether? **£4.40**

£1.50   £2.90

3 A parcel arrives at Gerry's house. It has two stamps on it, a £2.50 and a 35p.
How much did the parcel cost to post? **£2.85**

£2.50   35p

4 Adam and his dad go to the cinema.
How much does it cost? **£7.20**
How much change does Adam's dad get from a £10 note? **£2.80**

Cinema tickets
Adults   £4.50
Children £2.70

5 Jade wants to buy the box of chocolates for her mum. She has £2.60.
How much more does she need? **90p**

£3.50

6 Josh buys both games. He pays with a £10 note.
How much change does he get?
50p

£5.90   £3.60

7

*I am a money note.
I am between £10 and £50.*

What am I?

£20

Number problems 9

1 In a bag there are 12 oranges. A box of oranges has double that number.

How many oranges are in a box? **24**

2 There are 18 girls in a class. There are half as many boys as girls in the class.

How many boys are in the class? **9**

3 There are twice as many people on the upper deck of a bus as on the lower deck.

On the lower deck there are 19 people.

How many people are on the upper deck? **38**

4 A gardener plants trees at a school. She plants 18 trees at the front and 17 trees at the back of the school.

How many trees does she plant altogether? **35**

5 A squirrel has 34 nuts. He eats half of them.

How many nuts does he have left? **17**

6 When playing a game of darts Euan scores 13, 18 and 4.

What is his total score? **35**

7

If you double me and then halve the answer you get 28.

What am I?

28

Time problems 3

1 A candle lasts for 1 hour. James lights the candle at 9 o'clock.

How long will the candle stay lit after 9:45?   **15 min**

2 A pie takes 35 minutes to cook. Maggy puts the pie in the oven at 10:50.

At what time will it be ready?   **11.25**

3 A bus starts a journey at 9:45. The journey ends at 10:20.

For how many minutes does the journey last?   **35 min**

4 In a triathlon Michelle swims for 25 minutes, runs for 15 minutes and cycles for 20 minutes.

How long does the whole race take?   **1 hour**

5 A train takes 25 minutes from London to Reading and 26 minutes from Reading to Bath.

How long does it take from London to Bath?

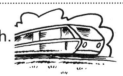

51 minutes

6 Tino runs a mile race in 5 minutes 15 seconds. That is 20 seconds slower than Annie.

How long did it take Annie to run the mile race?   **4 minutes 55 seconds**

7

My hours are double 4. My minutes are half of 40.

What am I?

8 hr 20 min

23

Weight problems 1

❶ Dale is baking. He uses 200 g out of a 1 kg packet of sugar.

How many grams of sugar are left? **800 g**

❷ A packet of crisps weighs 25 g.

What is the weight of two packets of crisps? **50 g**

❸ A packet of 5 tea bags weighs 25 g.

How much does one tea bag weigh? **5 g**

❹ Jamie buys the two pieces of cheese.

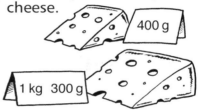

What is the total weight of the two pieces of cheese? **1 kg 700 g**

❺ At birth a puppy weighs 600 g. After 1 year it has increased its weight by 500 g.

How much does the puppy weigh after 1 year? **1 kg 100 g**

❻ A jar of jam weighs 400 g. How many kilograms do 5 jars weigh? **2 kg**

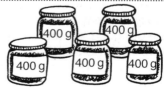

❼ *My two digits are the same. Each digit is one-half of 10.*

What am I?

55

Teachers' Notes

Contents

Introduction

The Pupil's books

Word Problems, a series of four books, one for each of the years 3 to 6, helps develop children's ability to solve number problems in a variety of contexts. Each page of word problems may be used to support numeracy lessons taught earlier in a week or for homework. The books provide weekly practice of word problems, as described in the National Numeracy Strategy (NNS) *Framework* and are designed to match the weekly structure within the NNS "sample medium-term plans". The style of questions reflects the examples that appear in the National Curriculum tests.

The books contain two types of page:

Topic pages: Each page has six word problems which are devoted solely to one Topic (Number, Money, Time, Length, Weight, Capacity and Measures). The overall mathematical content of all the Topic pages is listed on page iii. The mathematical content of the word problems on each page is listed in the lozenge at the top of the page.

Question 7 on each Topic page is a number puzzle, which gives children practice in Reasoning with Number using a variety of number properties. These questions are similar to those in the *Framework* and the National Curriculum tests.

Review pages look back at the mathematical content of previous Topic pages. Some Review pages are double page spreads, with the left page having a scene with information that is required to answer questions, and the right page asking questions about the scene.

Illustrations are used to tune children in to the 'real life' context of the word problem. Each is part of the problem and it is important that children look at the illustrations closely. An illustration may contain information that is also in the word problem itself. On other occasions an illustration will contain information that is <u>not</u> in the text of the word problem, but is essential in order to solve the problem.

Answers to word problems are printed in red at the side of each question in the pupils' pages of the Teachers' notes.

Helping children solve word problems

Here are some suggestions for helping children develop a strategy for solving word problems.

- Make sure children read a question carefully and not merely search for key words such as 'altogether' which they think, sometimes incorrectly, tell them what to do with the numbers.

- Encourage children to close their eyes and picture the context of a problem and any actions that are performed with/on 'objects' in the context.

- Allow children to talk with other children about a problem and to ask themselves:

  - 'What do I have to find out?'

  - 'What do I know that will help me find out?'

  - 'What do I have to do with what I know to find out?'

It is also important as part of a word problem solving strategy that children develop:

- the skill of recognising information that is helpful and that which is not helpful when trying to solve a word problem.

- the ability to choose and use appropriate operations to solve word problems

These can only develop with experience of solving many word problems over a long period of time.

Teaching plans

So that you can integrate *Word Problems* into your medium-term teaching plans pages iv to vi show the relationship between the Topics in *Word Problems* and the Sample Medium-term plans suggested by the NNS. Pages vii and viii show how the Topics in *Word Problems* relate to Mathematics in the National Curriculum in Wales Programme of Study and the similar Programme of Study for Northern Ireland.

Summary of mathematical content

page	topic	Mathematical content
4	Number 1	place value; more/less; $+10/-100$
5	Money 1	totals and change; multiplication facts to 5×5
6	Number 2	doubles/halves; near doubles; bridging through multiple of 10
7	Time 1	multiples of 5 min; $5\times$ and $\div$ facts
8	Number 3	$+/-$ facts to 10; pairs that make 20
9	Length 1	m/cm relationship; mixed units; $2\times$, $10\times$ and $\div$ facts
10–11	**Review 1**	**review of previous content**
12	Number 4	odd/even; repeated addition; arrays; $+/-$ facts to 20
13	Money 2	totals and change; multiples of 100 make 1000
14	Number 5	multiplication by 10/100; 10/100 more or less
15	Number 6	unit fractions; fractions of quantities; doubles/halves
16	Time 2	relationships between units; near doubles
17	Number 7	small differences; $2\times$, $5\times$, $10\times$ and $\div$ facts
18–19	**Review 2**	**review of previous content**
20	Number 8	more/less; $+/-$ facts to 20
21	Money 3	totals and change; multiples of 10 make 100
22	Number 9	doubles/halves; near doubles; add several numbers
23	Time 3	time to 5 minutes; near doubles
24	Weight 1	kg/g relationship; mixed units; 2 and $5\times$ and $\div$ facts
25	Measures 1	four operations; $\times/\div$ by 10
26–27	**Review 3**	**review of previous content**
28	Number 10	number puzzles; doubles; count in 3s, 4s or 5s
29	Money 4	totals and change; $+/-$ facts to 20; multiples of 100 make 1000; multiples of 5 make 100
30	Number 11	HTU+HTU; grouping/sharing
31	Number 12	equivalent fractions; 2, 3 and $5\times$ and $\div$ facts
32	Number 13	multi-step
33	**Review 4**	**review of previous content**
34	Number 14	more/less; doubles/halves
35	Money 5	totals and change; doubles/halves
36	Number 15	HTU+TU/HTU; add several numbers; $+/-$ near multiples of 10
37	Capacity 1	L/mL relationship; mixed units; $+/-$ facts to 20; multiples of 100 make 1000
38	Measures 2	four operations; $2\times$, $5\times$ and $\div$ facts; multiples of 5 make 100
39	Measures 3	four operations; $3\times$, $10\times$ and $\div$ facts
40–41	**Review 5**	**review of previous content**
42	Number 16	number puzzles; multiples of 2, 5, 10, 50 and 100
43	Money 6	totals and change; $+/-$ facts to 20; order amounts
44	Number 17	HTU+HTU; doubles/halves
45	Number 18	compare fractions; multiples of 100 make 1000; multiples of 5 make 100
46	Time 4	calendar; $+/-$ near multiples of 10; $\times/\div$ 2 and 5
47	Number 19	TU/HTU-TU; use known facts; $4\times$ and $\div$ facts
48	**Review 6**	**review of previous content**

Word Problems and the National Numeracy Strategy
Sample medium-term plans

AUTUMN			
Sample medium-term plans		**Word Problems**	
Unit	Topic	Pages	Topic
1	Place value, ordering, estimating, rounding Reading numbers from scales	4	Number 1
2–3	Understanding + and − Mental calculation strategies (+ and −) Money and 'real life' problems Making decisions, checking results	5–6	Money 1 Number 2
4–6	Measures, including problems Shape and space Reasoning about shapes	7–9	Time 1 Number 3 Length 1
7	**Assess and review**	**10–11**	**Review 1**
8	Counting, properties of numbers Reasoning about numbers	12	Number 4
9–10	Understanding × and ÷ Mental calculation strategies (× and ÷) Money and 'real life' problems Making decisions, checking results	13–14	Money 2 Number 5
11	Fractions	15	Number 6
12	Understanding + and − Mental calculation strategies (+ and −) Time, including problems Making decisions, checking results	16	Time 2
13	Handling data	17	Number 7
14	**Assess and review**	**18–19**	**Review 2**

SPRING			
Sample medium-term plans		Word Problems	
Unit	Topic	Pages	Topic
1	Place value, ordering, estimating, rounding Reading numbers from scales	20	Number 8
2–3	Understanding + and − Mental calculation strategies (+ and −) Money and 'real life' problems Making decisions, checking results	21–22	Money 3 Number 9
4–6	Shape and space Reasoning about shapes Measures, and time, including problems	23–25	Time 3 Weight 1 Measures 1
7	Assess and review	26–27	Review 3
8	Counting, properties of numbers Reasoning about numbers	28	Number 10
9–10	Understanding + and − Mental calculation strategies (+ and −) Understanding × and ÷ Mental calculation strategies (× and ÷) Money and 'real life' problems Making decisions, checking results	29–30	Money 4 Number 11
11	Fractions	31	Number 12
12	Handling data	32	Number 13
13	Assess and review	33	Review 4

SUMMER			
Sample medium-term plans		**Word Problems**	
Unit	Topic	Pages	Topic
1	Place value, ordering, estimating, rounding Reading numbers from scales	34	Number 14
2–3	Understanding + and − Mental calculation strategies (+ and −) Money and 'real life' problems Making decisions, checking results Pencil and paper procedures	35–36	Money 5 Number 15
4–6	Measures, including problems Shape and space Reasoning about shapes	37–39	Capacity 1 Measures 2 Measures 3
7	**Assess and review**	40–41	**Review 5**
8	Counting, properties of numbers Reasoning about numbers	42	Number 16
9–10	Understanding × and ÷ Mental calculation strategies (× and ÷) Money and 'real life' problems Making decisions, checking results	43–44	Money 6 Number 17
11	Fractions	45	Number 18
12	Understanding + and − Mental calculation strategies (+ and −) Pencil and paper procedures Time, including problems Making decisions, checking results	46	Time 4
13	Handling data	47	Number 19
14	**Assess and Review**	48	**Review 6**

Word Problems and the National Curriculum in Wales

Using and Applying Mathematics
U1. Making and Monitoring Decisions to Solve
    Problems
U2. Developing Mathematical Language and
    Communication
U3. Developing Mathematical Reasoning

Number
N1. Understanding Number and Place Value
N2. Understanding Number Relationships and Methods
    of Calculation
N3. Solving Numerical Problems
Shape, Space and Measures
S3. Understanding and Using Measures

Word Problems and the National Curriculum in Northern Ireland

PROCESSES IN MATHEMATICS
P1. Using Mathematics
P2. Communicating Mathematically
P3. Mathematical Reasoning
MEASURES (M)

NUMBER
N1. Understanding Number and Number Notation
N2. Patterns, Relationships, and Sequences
N3. Operations and their Applications
N4. Money

page	topic	P1	P2	P3	N1	N2	N3	N4	M
4	Number 1	x	x	x	x		x		
5	Money 1	x	x	x				x	
6	Number 2	x	x	x		x	x		
7	Time 1	x	x	x					x
8	Number 3	x	x	x			x		
9	Length 1	x	x	x					x
10–11	Review 1	x	x	x		x	x	x	x
12	Number 4	x	x	x		x	x		
13	Money 2	x	x	x				x	
14	Number 5	x	x	x	x		x		
15	Number 6	x	x	x	x	x			
16	Time 2	x	x	x					x
17	Number 7	x	x	x			x		
18–19	Review 2	x	x	x		x	x	x	x
20	Number 8	x	x	x	x	x	x		
21	Money 3	x	x	x				x	
22	Number 9	x	x	x		x	x		
23	Time 3	x	x	x					x
24	Weight 1	x	x	x					x
25	Measures 1	x	x	x					x
26–27	Review 3	x	x	x		x	x	x	x
28	Number 10	x	x	x		x	x		
29	Money 4	x	x	x				x	
30	Number 11	x	x	x			x		
31	Number 12	x	x	x	x		x		
32	Number 13	x	x	x			x		
33	Review 4	x	x	x		x	x	x	x
34	Number 14	x	x	x	x	x			
35	Money 5	x	x	x		x		x	
36	Number 15	x	x	x			x		
37	Capacity 1	x	x	x					x
38	Measures 2	x	x	x					x
39	Measures 3	x	x	x					x
40–41	Review 5	x	x	x		x	x	x	x
42	Number 16	x	x	x			x		
43	Money 6	x	x	x				x	
44	Number 17	x	x	x		x	x		
45	Number 18	x	x	x	x		x		
46	Time 4	x	x	x					x
47	Number 19	x	x	x			x		
48	Review 6	x	x	x		x	x	x	x

Measures problems 1

❶ In a pack there are 10 cans. Each can has 200 mL of juice.

How many litres of juice are there altogether in the pack? **2 L**

❷ When training for a race Gaby runs 3 km 500 m and jogs for 2 km 500 metres.

How many kilometres does she train for? **6 km**

❸ Bob does 10 step-ups every minute.

How long does it take Bob to do 100 step-ups? **10 minutes**

❹ Alice weighs out 3 kg of flour. This is 200 g more than she needs.

How much flour does she need? **2 kg 800 g**

❺ Jelena with her clothes on weighs 26 kg. Her clothes weigh 2 kg. A year later, without clothes, she weighs 29 kg.

By how many kilograms has her weight increased in the year? **5 kg**

❻ A balloon flies 100 km each hour.

How far will the balloon fly in 10 hours? **1000 km**

❼  *1 more than me is one-half of 500.* What am I?

249

25

Review problems 3

1 The swimming pool has 6 lanes.
In which lane is the swimmer who is first? **5**
In which lane is the swimmer who is last? **4**

2 The length of the pool is 50 metres.
The race is 2 lengths of the pool.
How long is the race?   **100 m**

3 The winner swims the first length in 31 sec and the second length in 29 sec.
How long did it take him to swim the whole race?   **1 min**

4 Another race is 400 metres long.
How many lengths of the pool is this?   **8**

5 Richard and his mum and dad are watching.
How much did it cost them to get in?   **£13.50**

6 Richard buys two lemon drinks.
How much do they cost him?   **50p**

7 How much more does an apple drink cost than orange?   **5p**

8 A bottle of lemon has 300 mL.
How many litres are in 10 bottles?   **3 L**

9 To get to the swimming pool Richard walked 2 km.
He then went on a bus for 17 km.
How far did he go to get to the pool?   **19 km**

10 To get his Whale badge Richard has to swim 4 lengths of the pool on his front and 4 lengths on his back.
What is the total length he has to swim?   **400 m**

Number problems 10

1 A pack has 3 cans. Deja puts 4 packs in a pile.

3 cans
3 cans
3 cans
3 cans

How many cans are in the 4 packs? **12**

2 Two schools have a cross-country race. Each school has 5 runners.

How many children are in the race? **10**

3 In each box there are 4 cakes.
How many cakes are there altogether?
24

4 4 4 4 4 4

4 There are 5 balls in a tube. Amy counts the number of balls in seven tubes.

5 balls

How many balls will she count altogether? **35**

5 I start at a number and count on 2 threes and then 2 fours. I end at 15.

What number did I start at? **1**

6 In a red box there are 10 crayons. In a blue box there are twice as many as in the red box.

How many crayons are in the blue box? **20**

10
CRAYONS

7

I am a two-digit multiple of 3 and 4. My tens digit is 4. What am I?

48

28

Money problems 4

totals and change;
+/− facts to 20;
multiples of 100 make 1000;
multiples of 5 make 100

1 In a sale the price of the toaster is £5 less than its normal £18.

How much is the toaster in the sale? **£13**

£18 less £5

2 The table costs £400. The four chairs cost £600.

What is the total cost of the table and chairs? **£1000**

3 Nyla buys a 9p toffee and an 8p lolly.

9p

8p

How much does she pay altogether? **17p**

4 Greg has 12p. He buys a 4p candy.

How much money has he left? **8p**

4p

5 Marie pays £1.30 for an ice cream and 60p for an ice lolly.

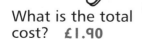

What is the total cost? **£1.90**

6 Simon has saved £6.50. He needs another £3.50 to buy a CD.

£6.50

How much is the CD? **£10**

7

I am two numbers. The total of my numbers is 1000. The difference between my two numbers is 100.

What am I?

450, 550

29

Number problems 11

① Laura has 20 flowers to put into four vases. She shares them equally between the vases.

How many flowers are in each vase? **5**

② A zoo has 248 animals. Another 100 animals are sent to the zoo.

How many animals are in the zoo now? **348**

③ In a nest there are 350 ants. At the end of the day 151 more ants return to the nest.

How many ants are in the nest at the end of the day? **501**

④ A class of 28 children are grouped into teams of 4.

How many teams are there? **7**

⑤ A supermarket sells 246 cans of drinks on a Monday. On Tuesday it sells 327.

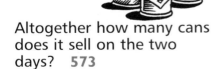

Altogether how many cans does it sell on the two days? **573**

⑥ At the end of a party 30 balloons are shared equally between 10 children.

How many balloons does each child get? **3**

⑦

I am a three-digit number. My tens digit is 4. My units digit is half my tens digit. My hundreds digit is double my tens digit.

What am I?

842

Number problems 12

1 In a dish there are 8 strawberries. Debbie eats half of them. Adam eats two-quarters of them.

Who eats more? **Neither**
Explain your answer.

2 In a game Javed scores 40 points in 8 equal scores.

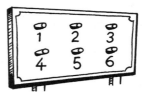

How many points does he score each time? **5**

3 A group of children is split into nine pairs.

How many children are in the group? **18**

4 Amy buys 5 stickers each week.

How many stickers has she at the end of 7 weeks? **35**

5 Joanne divides a bag of 14 apples equally between herself and her brother.

How many apples does her brother get? **7**

14 apples

6 Each packet has 3 cakes. Betsy buys 8 packets.

How many cakes does Betsy buy? **24**

7

*I am a three-digit number.
The three digits are all different and in order, largest first.
Each digit is a multiple of 3.*

What am I?

963

31

Number problems 13

1 Bill has 7 toy racing cars. Clara has double what Bill has. Clara gives Bill 3 of her cars.
How many cars has Clara left?   **11**

2 Harry buys a packet of 24 chews. He eats four of them and shares the rest equally between his 5 sisters.
How many chews does each get?   **4**

3 There are 17 cars in a car park. Nine of the cars leave and 6 more come in.
How many cars are in the car park now?   **14**

4 Sarah's mum has 2 packets of 8 ice lollies in the freezer. Sarah eats 2 of the ice lollies.
How many are left?   **14**

5 Jackie has 15 bird cards. She buys 5 packets of the bird cards. She finds she has 7 repeats so she gives them away.
How many has she left?   **58**

6 Javed buys and sells stamps. He already has 30 stamps. He buys 10 packets of 5 stamps. Then he puts all his stamps into packets of 5.
How many packets does he make?   **16**

7

When I am subtracted from 80 the answer is double 35.

What am I?

10

Review problems 4

1 A jumbo jet holds 400 passengers.
How many passengers can fit on 2 jumbo jets? **800**
How many passengers are on a jumbo jet when it is half full? **200**

2 A jumbo jet flies best when it is 10 000 metres high.
How many kilometres is 10 000 metres? **10 km**

3 An 8-year-old can cycle at about 9 kilometres each hour. A jumbo jet can travel at 100 times this speed.
How many kilometres can a jumbo jet do in 1 hour? **900 km**

4 In 1 minute the fuel tanker could fill up the petrol tanks of 40 cars. A petrol tank of a car holds 50 litres.
How many litres can the fuel tanker put in the jumbo jet in one minute? **2000 L**

5 For a long flight the jumbo jet is loaded with 800 meals. The jumbo jet has 400 passengers.
How many meals can each passenger have? **2**

6 A Concorde plane takes 3 hours to fly from London to New York. A jumbo jet takes twice as long.
How long does it take for a jumbo jet to fly from London to New York? **6 hours**

7

*I am between 80 and 90.
When you count on in fives starting at 0 you will say me.*

What am I?

85

Number problems 14

1 A red book has 273 pages. A blue book has 142 pages.

Which book has more pages? **red**
How many more? **131**

2 In four games Jade scores 489, 483, 469 and 498 points.

Which was the most points Jade scored? **498**
Which was the least points Jade scored? **469**

3 Gaby takes 35 strides to walk the length of the playground. Her brother takes twice as many strides.

How many strides did Gaby's brother take? **70**

4 Danny has a packet of 90 chocolate buttons. He eats half of them.

How many chocolate buttons does Danny have left? **45**

5 Paul is looking for his friend's home. He knows that it is an odd number between 159 and 163.

What number is it? **161**

6 With ten darts Sarah scores 205 points. Matthew scores 250 points with ten darts.

Who scored fewer points? **Sarah**
How many fewer? **45**

7 I am a two-digit number.
I am a multiple of 5 and 3.
The difference between my digits is 1.

What am I?

45

34

Money problems 5

❶ Roy buys a violin for £120 and a trumpet for £80.

How much does he pay altogether for the two instruments? **£200**

❷ Sean sees the fishing rod for sale. He has £70.

How much more does he need? **£19.50**

❸ Claire gets £1.50 pocket money each week. On her birthday her dad gives her twice as much.

How much does her dad give her on her birthday? **£3.00**

❹ Matt saves 50p each week to buy the game Blitz.

How many weeks will it take to save enough money to buy the game? **9**

❺ Jenny and her mum and dad go to the cinema.

What is the total cost?
£9

Prices
Adults £3.50
Children £2.00

❻ Paula has £3. She spends half of it. Her mother then gives her 50p.

How much money does Paula have now? **£2**

❼ *I am more than £1.50 and less than £4.50. My amount in pence is a multiple of 3 and 50.*

What am I?

£3.00

Number problems 15

HTU+TU/HTU;
add several numbers;
+/– near multiples of 10

1 There are 3 people on a bus. At the next three stops 3, 5 and 4 more people get on the bus.

How many people are on the bus now?   **15**

2 At the start of a film there are 39 children in the cinema. Soon 41 more have joined them.

How many children are in the cinema now?   **80**

3 Lenny gets 67 full glasses of juice ready for a party. Only 39 glasses are drunk.
How many full glasses are left?   **28**

4 Khadim has 286 stamps in his album. He buys 33 more stamps. How many stamps does he now have?   **319**

5 In the first game Tricia scores 127 points. In the second game she scores 455 points.

How many points does she score altogether?   **582**

6 There are 56 trees in a wood. In a conservation project children plant another 19 trees.

How many trees are in the wood at the end of the project?   **75**

7

My 3 digits are odd and increase in size. All three digits are different. The sum of the digits is 9.

What am I?

135

36

Capacity problems 1

L/mL relationship;
mixed units;
+/− facts to 20;
multiples of 100 make 1000

❶ Lauren makes 17 litres of juice for a party. Her friends drink 12 litres.
How many litres of juice are left? **5 L**

17 litres

❷ Dino mixes 800 mL of plant food in a bucket. He then mixes another 200 mL.
How many millilitres has he made altogether? **1000 mL**

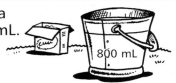

800 mL

❸ Each bottle has 1 L 500 mL of lemonade.

1 L
500 mL

How many litres of lemonade are there in four bottles? **6 L**

❹ Gary is painting the house. He uses 7 litres of paint. He then uses another 8 litres.

How many litres did he use altogether? **15 L**

❺ A petrol can when full holds 10 litres. There are 3 L 300 mL in the can.

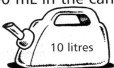

10 litres

How much more petrol is needed to fill it? **6 L 700 mL**

❻ Ross has a cold. He has had 15 mL of medicine. He is given another 5 mL.

5 mL

How many millilitres has he had altogether? **20 mL**

❼

Double me is 8 less than 40.

What am I?

16

Measures problems 2

1 Ario cuts a 1 metre piece of ribbon into five equal lengths.

How many centimetres long is each piece?   **20 cm**

2 Helen makes some Rice Crispie buns. She weighs out 85 g and then another 15 g.

How many grams of Rice Crispies does she weigh?   **100 g**

3 A bottle holds 1 L 500 mL of water. A larger bottle holds twice as much water.

How many litres of water does the larger bottle hold?   **3 L**

4 Every morning it takes Barrie 15 minutes to walk to school.

How long does he spend walking to school in a week?   **75 min**

5 Justin weighs out 3 kilograms of sugar. He divides the sugar equally into two basins.

How much sugar is in each basin?   **1500 g**

6 A train stops at the first station after 35 minutes. After 65 minutes it stops at the second station.

How long after the start is it before it stops for the second time?   **1 hr 40 min**

7

I belong to the 2, 3 and 4 times-tables. The sum of my two digits is 9.

What am I?

36

38

Measures problems 3

❶ A pack has 10 jars of beetroot. One jar weighs 300 grams.

What is the total weight of the pack? **3 kg**

300 g

---

❷ The length of a cycle race is three times around the streets of a town. The race is 36 kilometres long.

How long is it once around the streets? **12 km**

---

❸ A test has 10 questions. It lasts 3 min 20 sec. Children have the same time to answer each question.

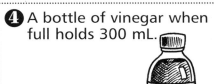

How long have the children to answer each question? **20 sec**

❹ A bottle of vinegar when full holds 300 mL.

300 mL

How many millilitres do 3 bottles hold? **900 mL**

---

❺ A 10 metre length of wood is marked out into 10 equal lengths.

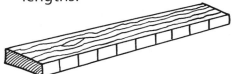

How many metres from one end is the third mark? **3 m**

❻ One bag of sugar weighs 1 kg. Jim opens three bags of sugar and divides it equally into ten bowls.

1 kg 1 kg 1 kg

How many grams of sugar are in each bowl? **300 g**

---

❼

Ten times me add 6 is 46.

What am I?

4

Review problems 5

Boats for hire

Pedal boats
£1.50 30min
Motor boats
£2.50 30min

Deck chairs £1.50
for half a day

Ice Cream

cornet	90p
99 cones	£1.10
orange lolly	75p
Buzz	£1.20

1 The Punch and Judy show has started. Six more children come to watch.
How many children are watching now? **16**

2 Rod hires a motor boat for 1 hour.
How much does it cost him? **£5**

3 Each pedal boat holds two people.
How many people would 8 pedal boats hold? **16**

4 John and Mary are building a sandcastle. John collects 4 buckets of water. Mary collects three times as many as John.
How many buckets of water does Mary collect? **12**

5 Each bucket of sand weighs 500 grams. It takes 10 buckets full to build a small castle.
How many kilograms of sand are needed for a small castle? **5 kg**

6 Meg spends exactly £4 on cornets and 99 cones.
How many cornets and 99 cones does she buy with the £4? **2 each**

7 Ada buys 2 cornets and 3 orange ice lollies.
What is the total cost? **£4.05**

8 Tom has £5. How many 99 cones can he buy? **4**
How much change would he get? **60p**

9 There are 6 donkeys. In 30 minutes each donkey carries 5 children.
How many children have a ride on 6 donkeys in one hour? **60**

10 A donkey ride is 10 metres up and 10 metres back.
How many times will a donkey have to go up and back to do 100 metres? **5**

11 What is the cost of a deck chair for a whole day? **£3**

❶ I am thinking of a number.
My number is the seventeenth multiple of 2.
What is my number?   **34**

❷ I am thinking of a number.
My number is the sum of the eighth and the eleventh multiple of 10.
What is my number?   **190**

❸ I am thinking of a number.
My number is one-half of the tenth multiple of 50.
What is my number?   **250**

❹ I am thinking of a number.
My number is 17 more than the fifth multiple of 100.
What is my number?   **517**

❺ I am thinking of a number.
My number is double the ninth multiple of 5.
What is my number?   **90**

❻ I am thinking of a number.
My number is the first multiple of both 5 and 100.
What is my number?   **100**

❼

I am two numbers. The sum of my numbers is 15. The difference between my numbers is 3.

What am I?

9, 6

Money problems 6

1 Alex's mum and dad look at some TVs.

What is the cost of the cheapest TV? **£357**

What is the cost of the dearest TV? **£381**

2 Kylie buys a soft rabbit for £13. She pays with a £20 note.

How much change does Kylie get? **£7**

3 Simon keeps pet snakes. He buys 3 snakes at £20 each.

How much does Simon pay altogether? **£60**

4 Four children go to the cinema. The total cost is £16.

What is the cost for one child? **£4**

5 Beth and her dad go swimming. It costs £4 for an adult and £2.50 for a child.

What is the total cost for Beth and her dad? **£6.50**

6 Christina has four £5 notes. She buys a toy monster for £7.

How much has Christina left? **£13**

7

If you add 7 to me and then take away 11 you will get 6.

What am I?

10

43

Number problems 17

❶ Each box has 15 golf balls.

How many golf balls are in two boxes? **30**

❷ Eighty children go on a school trip. One-half of the children are boys.

How many girls go on the trip? **40**

❸ I think of a number.
Double my number plus 8 is 82.
What is my number? **37**

❹ The Odeon cinema has 250 seats.
The Regal has double that number.
How many seats are in the Regal? **500**

❺ In a bottle bank there are 700 bottles. Half of the bottles are green.

How many bottles are not green? **350**

❻ Alice sells 250 raffle tickets. Holly sells 149.

How many tickets do Alice and Holly sell altogether? **399**

❼

*Both my hundreds and units digits
are one-half of my tens digit.
The sum of my three digits is 16.*

What am I?

484

Number problems 18

compare fractions; multiples of 100 make 1000; multiples of 5 make 100

1 Street School hope that 1000 people will come to the school fair. At the opening only 400 have come.

How many more have to come to make 1000? **600**

2 Mary eats $\frac{1}{3}$ of a cake. Bill eats $\frac{1}{4}$ of the cake.
Who eats more of the cake? **Mary**
Write about how you found out.

3 There are 85 hens on a farm. The farmer buys another 15 hens.

How many hens does the farmer have now? **100**

4 There are 200 people at the afternoon circus show. In the evening there are 800 people.

How many people are at the two shows altogether? **1000**

5 Marc has a box of jelly babies. He eats $\frac{1}{10}$ of them. Adam eats $\frac{1}{2}$ of them and Jessica eats $\frac{1}{5}$ of them.
Who eats the most sweets? **Adam**

6 A hundred children have school dinners. Thirty-five bring sandwiches.

How many more children have dinners than bring sandwiches? **65**

7  *My tens digit is half the sum of my other two digits. My units digit is 8 more than my hundreds digit.*

What am I?

159

45

Time problems 4

calendar;
+/– near multiples of 10;
×/÷ 2 and 5

❶

What day comes 19 days after a Monday?   **Saturday**

❷ The months of July and August have 31 days.

How many days are there from 1st July to 31st August?   **62**

❸ Each team in a cycle relay race has 6 riders. Each rider rides for 5 hours. The race starts at 9 a.m. on a Saturday.

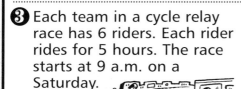

When does the race end?   **Sunday 3 p.m.**

❹

What is the date 21 days before 10th October?   **19th Sept**

❺ A man starts work on 1st July. He works for 5 days and rests for 5 days all the month.

For how many days does he rest between 1st July and 31st July?   **15**

❻ In 1994 Sarah's birthday was on Thursday, 10th February.
On what day was her birthday in 1995?   **Friday**
Which day was it in 1993?   **Wednesday**

❼ *I am a day of the week. The number of letters in my name is not a multiple of 2, nor a multiple of 3.*

What am I?

Tuesday

Number problems 19

❶ There are 253 children in a school hall. Six more children arrive late.
How many children are in the hall now? **259**

❷ A box has 57 straws. At a party 25 of them are used.
How many straws are left in the box? **32**

❸ In four games of skittles Amy scores 8 points in each game.

How many points does she score altogether? **32**

❹ A trawler catches 138 crabs. The fisherman puts 50 of the crabs back into the sea.

How many crabs are left? **88**

❺ At a zoo there are 24 monkeys. The monkeys are divided equally between four enclosures.

How many monkeys are there in each enclosure? **6**

❻ Australia score 407 runs. This is 10 more runs than England score.

AUSTRALIA RUNS
407

How many runs did England score? **397**

❼

I am a multiple of 4 and 5.
I am between 21 and 59.

What am I?

40

Review problems 6

1 In a 400 metres race Sumi finishes 7 metres behind the winner.

How far has Sumi run when the winner passes the winning post? **393 m**

2 Ketchup in a bottle weighs 500 grams.

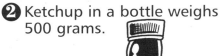

What is the total weight of ketchup in four bottles? **2 kg**

3 Jenny sends two parcels by post. One costs £2.70, the other costs £1.90.

What is the total cost of the two parcels? **£4.60**

4 A litre of juice is poured equally into two bottles.

How many millilitres of juice are in each bottle? **500 mL**

5 Joe catches a train at 12 o'clock. The journey lasts for 1 hr 30 min. He then takes a bus and gets home at 2 p.m.

How long does the bus journey take? **30 min**

6 A packet has 20 biscuits. Four packets are put into a box. Sam eats six of the biscuits.

How many biscuits are left in the box? **74**

7

Three more than me is double 20.

What am I?

37

48